Music

IN THE LIFE OF

Albert Schweitzer